Tales From Santa's Album*

by the

Elves Themselves

*With Prologue and footnotes from the pen of Mrs. A. B. Claus

Printed in Canada

Thanks to Mark Davidson at Mark Davidson Photography,
Palm Springs, California for the photos of the elves.

ISBN 978-1-77136-117-0

FIN 25 03 13

To those who are with us

and

Those who are not

and

For Grace Elaine Tew and

her wonderful family

Thanks:

To my partner and husband Bill

for his unfailing enthusiasm and encouragement,

my sister Susan

for her typing and ever helpful comments, and

my great friend Alice Linden

whose time and expertise I called on so often.

The elves became "our boys"

- AV

Prologue

The

Triplet Trilogy

This was the year the boys wanted to live in their own cottage – and what an adventure THAT turned out to be!

Their Mother got them into the old traditional costumes and caps for the annual photos – I thought they looked darling. Santa wonders if they are a bit young to be asking to drive the sleigh, but Nelwyn is very responsible – they will be just fine.

We all smile now to think back on the snarl that Selwyn's illness caused, but it all worked out......

Selwyn

Story 1

The Seniors
Save Christmas

(Selwyn's late night adventure)

Birdseye View of the North Pole

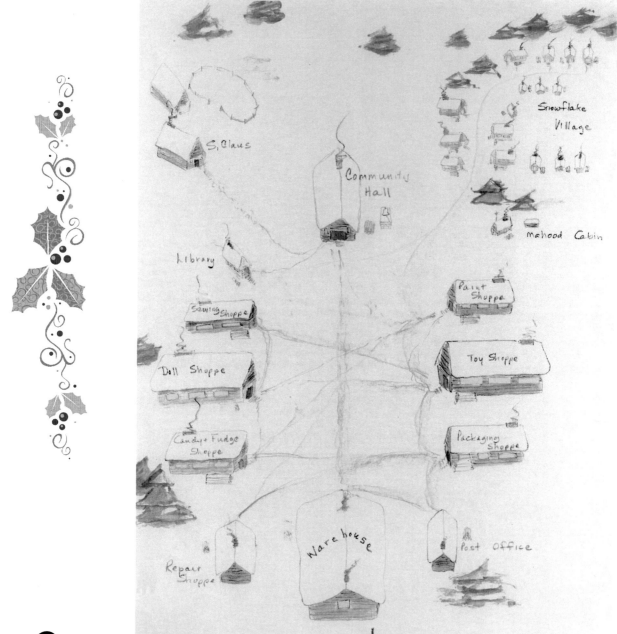

Mr. and Mrs. Claus sit warming by a toasty, dwindling fire in their snug cottage.

The reindeer have been bedded down in their stalls, heavy-lidded, heads hanging after their round-the-world dash. Why, what a night it had been! Snow over Denver, rain over rural England and thousands of clear, cold, starry miles between Canada and Tasmania! The team never faltered; Santa thought to himself – an evening's work very well done indeed.

Murmuring quietly to each other, the Claus' tried to comprehend yet again, the events that had almost overwhelmed them the week before Christmas. How close they had come to disaster, they marveled. How close they had come to disappointing all the little children of the world who believed in them.

This is what they recalled:

The year began well......

Late winter and spring were golden and dry,
The North Pole was gladdened by birds on the fly.
Windows were polished and mirrors gleamed bright,
Santa loved spring – it was such a sweet sight

To see tools and benches all ordered and clear
"Job well done, elves, he boomed, "Now it's on to next year!"
In May, an orderly "way" starts to move –
Time to nudge Next Christmas into its groove.

Santa's praise and the thanks of the world's little tots
Stimulate elf brains with myriad thoughts!
Now, young elves apprentice to follow their Dads,
After years of practice these likable lads

Are promoted to workshops and projects galore
Where their ideas, talent and competence soar!
The elvas, likewise, are taught by their Mothers
To finish the goods made by uncles and brothers.

They mix all the colour, sew costumes, print labels
Then package up goods on long workshop tables.
By June, the Elf Masters had schedules in place.
Committees had formed – ideas raced!

Agents in ports all over the globe
Began to procure a mountainous trove

of ribbons and puzzles and toys of all kinds,
Designed to drive little ones out of their minds!

Christmas Island, Reindeer Lake, and Noel called in,
Santa Fe, Santa Ana and Santa Cruz had been
Waiting to share what they saw as hot trends
In giftware for giving to family and friends.

Logistical bookkeepers working in pairs
Directed deliveries up and down warehouse stairs.
Products amassing on all of the shelves
Amazed and delighted the tiniest elves.

Last summer had been special, a coming of age
For the teenaged triplets, turning a page
In the Book of Life: they wanted a place of their own
Away from the routine they'd known at home.

Triplets worldwide are a rare thing, and good!
Their father taught shop skills and found that they could
Help each other grasp work in a trice,
Teach one – teach three –wonderfully nice!

So in July, a new cabin went up at the Pole
For these bachelor elves whose foremost goal
Was to live near the workshops so they could pitch in
If workers fell ill or got backlogged within.

There was hewing and sawing and hammering 'til
This brand new dwelling was ready to fill.
A three-tiered bunk in knotty pine wood
Awaited Nelwyn and Welwyn and Selwyn Mahood.

The Yoga Masters made rounds in the heat
Of August – reminding them all that to beat
The stress of Next Christmas' last second race,
Meditation and stretching could help slow the pace.

Strength coaches came by in early September
Promoting fitness so each would remember
That as the pace began to quicken
Endurance was needed so as not to sicken.

The weeks of the calendar started to slide
The elves were enjoying their creative side!
Projects took off as the orders poured in,
Santa's workshops were humming and joy reigned within.

Workouts at dawn, tai chi, and long hikes,
Karaoke and poetry readings at night.
Lots of diversions to make life fun
And maintain the rhythm in days to come.

Their motto was this: "when stress starts to bother,
Elves and elvas alike are to help one another".
October flew by in a massive hurry
Shelves were piled high with toys shiny and furry.

Daylight got shorter and orders lengthened,
Quitting early was never mentioned.
The triplets worked hard through the brisk fall weather.
Their parents thanked Santa, who'd kept them together.

Nelwyn and Welwyn bulked up and grew strong
Watching for Selwyn tagging along.
Slight of stature, this youngest of three
Was honest and loyal and as smart as could be.

The three worked beautifully side by side
Completely content to discuss and abide.
December arrived, gales started to blow,
Icicles lengthened and trails filled with snow.

Out on a hike with his brothers one day
Young Selwyn Mahood – battling sleet – lost his way.
He plunged on in search of the end of the trail
But the ice felt like needles and turned into hail.

Soaking and cold, bedraggled to boot,
He muttered, "I must finish this miserable route".
His body was freezing, his teeth all a-chatter,
The others turned back and found him – a matter

Of urgency – obvious to all –
For the young elf had slipped and curled into a ball.
Nelwyn and Welwyn and a posse of friends
At last got Selwyn, with capable hands

Back to their cabin – ruing the hail –
"We must warm you up or tomorrow you'll fail".
They built up the fire and bedded him down,
Snuggly blankets were tucked all around.

They brought him cups of honeyed tea
But looking in they could clearly see
That Selwyn was flushed;
His breathing was raspy;
He was

      coming down

           with something……..

                      nasty

      Hours passed.
Selwyn was burning with fever so hot
That chills and shaking were rocking the cot.
Nelwyn and Welwyn moved out of their beds
Needing somewhere quiet to lay their heads.
After their day, which had started so well,
They were upset and frightened seeing Selwyn so ill.

Past ten and eleven the fever raged on
Young Selwyn awoke – befuddled and wan –
His hair was disheveled, his breathing was tight
In his bloodshot eyes there glittered a light:

He knew not the day, nor the place, nor the hour
But felt that he held in his hands all the power
To work through the night to make up for lost time:
Letting down Santa would feel like a crime.

He struggled from bed and lurched down the hall,
Out the side door, in darkness, he suffered a fall.
His feverish brow was a-glisten with sweat,
His jammies were clammy and wrinkly wet.

One slipper fell off and the other got lost -
Where to start? What to do? His brain felt all tossed.
He began in Paint Shoppe with trembling hand
And mixed all the colours, in one vat, WITH SAND!

Doll houses and wagons emerged lined and streaky,
Surf boards and skis looked blatantly freaky.
Gritty paint blobs covered the floor
Then choking fumes forced him to head for the door.

On to the Toy Shoppe – trying so hard to help –
He dropped hammer and glue gun – heard himself yelp -
He tried to bolt see-saws and swing sets together
Neglecting the blueprints traced clearly on leather.

Selwyn's swings didn't swing and his teeters didn't totter,
He felt weak and unhappy, grew sicker and hotter,
But dug deep in his heart for the strength to go on
And finish some packing 'fore night turned to dawn.

He bubble-wrapped sleds for Chattanooga –

Snorkels were boxed up to go to Iowa.

Malamute harnesses destined for Nome
Were hazily, dazedly tagged for Rome.

Mittens and earmuffs were heading to Jamaica!

Nails mixed with candies and coloured balloons
Were added to stockings with ribbons festooned.

Little Selwyn labored on in the darkness.......

When Nelwyn and Welwyn awoke after four,
They noticed the silence and leaped to the floor.
The rattling cough and occasional moan
Had stopped – was their little brother......*gone?*

His cot was empty, his robe on the stair,
They followed his trail to the side door with care.
Snowflakes were falling and covered the tops
Of faint footprints – lurching out t'ward the Shoppes.

Nelwyn, the eldest, was quiet and strong.
Welwyn, the dreamer, was usually calm,
            but

When they peeked through the frosty window of the Packaging Shoppe, alarm in their eyes, they saw Selwyn, exhausted, slump to the floor.

Nelwyn swept into that wreck of a room and gathered his younger brother into his arms. Welwyn quickly knelt beside them and tucked his bathrobe around his brother's body. Tenderly, three heads bent together, the older boys gently lifted him home.

Their cheeks were wet.

What could be done?

There was only one week left until Christmas!

Nelwyn made a decision at once. Off to Santa's cabin he raced with the dreadful news, then to the Community Hall where he manfully hauled on the heavy rope that rang the huge brass Alarm Bell.

Dawn broke.

Quietly, steadily, up through the trees, elves and elvas in twos and threes gathered around Santa, rubbing sleep from their tired eyes and pulling shawls more tightly around their shoulders.

From Shoppe to Shoppe they slowly walked.

The elders circled, together they talked.

"On Santa's broad shoulders a Christmas tale rests,

He never has wavered, has given his best,

To rectify things is a job for the elves –

We'll agree on swift action and do it ourselves.

Many hands we can offer and happily so,

We seniors have time and the patience to go

Into the Shoppes with never a frown –

Let us help Santa – we'll NOT let him down".

So, as the graybeards were taught to do, they
1. surveyed and assessed the damage. Calling on their memories and experience, they
2. formed a plan. Then, agreed on a common goal, they
3. vowed to work together –

For the children!

Gently brightening, that day softly began
Younger elves heard their elders – applauded the plan.
Whatever was needed was what would be done,
Setbacks they'd manage, the day would be won.

Tho' aged and stooped, their wisdom loomed large,
They calmly stepped forward and firmly took charge;
"Disaster befell us in nineteen ought two –
We learned working in shifts was the best thing to do.

The Shoppes unaffected must go on, we pray,
So that orders received can be processed today.
Half the Seniors shall go to the Paint Shoppe at once –
The first shift starts now and will work through 'til lunch."

In order that Mothers could help by the day,
Mrs. Claus took the babies and set them to play
On her kitchen floor, all cosy and warm,
Rocked them and watched that they came to no harm.

In Paint Shoppe, the Grandpas and Grandmas and Grans
Set about sanding with arthritic hands

The doll houses, wagons and surf boards too,
Slathered with Selwyn's abhorrent hues.

As the first shift went home for lunch and a nap,
The second moved in and took up the slack.
Since their daughters and sons worked as hard as they might
These elders determined to put things right!

They unbolted cockeyed playground swings
And reassembled these popular things.
Surely, securely, they steadily gained
Following blueprints 'til daylight waned.

The teeters tottered and all was well.
The Toy Shoppe still hummed as twilight fell.
Pleased with their efforts but achy and spent,
They called it a day. Off homeward they went.

The elders inquired of the Senior Mahoods –
All hoped Selwyn was out of the woods.

At the end of five days, Santa summoned his teams,
Cautiously, he declared that little tots' dreams
Would likely be met at Christmas this year
Several of those present shed a quiet tear.

Including Santa who acknowledged his elves
For giving so unselfishly of themselves;

The alarm they'd felt before they took action
Had now been replaced with sweet satisfaction.

Tomorrow – together – they would all start the day
By moving to "Packing" where the next challenge lay
In re-routing ski gear all set to go
To hemispheres totally lacking in snow –
And the like. They knew now that they could finish by Christmas Eve.

So while elders re-addressed the gift tags galore,
Wee elfins sat at their feet on the floor
To untangle ribbon and unstick tape
Then pile all the sweepings to the sides of the grate.

Last but not least came the ticklish part –
Taking the colourful stockings apart;
Small gifties destined for females or males
Had been lovingly sprinkled – by Selwyn – with NAILS!

Sparkling accents in crackers and horns
Would brighten everyone's Christmas morn –
[Or so Selwyn thought in his delirious state......
To his fevered eyes, each sharp nail point glimmered with a golden halo of light
– these Christmas stockings were going to be the most beautiful ever seen; why,
the Villagers would NEVER forget THIS Christmas!]

Seniors opened a blanket, then the elfins were asked
If they would help out with this sensitive task:
Could they carry the stockings and empty them all
On to this coverlet stretched to the wall?

Shyly they nodded, glad to be part
Of this Christmas project in everyone's heart,
They worked intently with humming and songs
Til an elder approached holding long-handled tongs.

The elfins were asked to move back; the pile of goodies was smoothed out into one layer with the tongs. Two Grandpas came forward to stand at one end of the blanket, each senior elf holding the end of a long black bar. Forward and backward they slowly walked, holding the bar low over the blanket.

The elfins were wide-eyed to see the shiny nails jump up and stick to the bar until it resembled a long, hairy, quivering, silvery beard – the elders had saved the day with A Magnet!

The elfins squealed with glee
For they could clearly see
That the candy pile was free –
    Of nails!

Each was presented with a treat and settled on the edge of the blanket. Each removed crayons, candy canes, suckers, whistles, horns and puzzles according to his or her ability...

- one elfine took out yellow balloons because she liked yellow.
- one removed only black whistles because he was certain of that colour.
- one only removed candy canes because she could hang the hooks over her wrist.
- And so it went until all the treats were separated.

All the stockings were lovingly repacked.

At the end of the week with relief in his voice
Santa gathered his workforce to heartily rejoice
In the total recovery of Selwyn Mahood,
Whose illness had shown them all that they could -
Working together – put everything right.
Christmas was saved and the future looked bright
        For the children!

Christmas Eve excitement filled the air – young elves danced for joy when they heard of the ingenious use of the magnet by their grandparents. Sparkling snowflakes fluttered down from the moon-filled sky. Snorting reindeer pawed in their stalls, impatient to be hitched to Santa's sleigh for this year's joyous, bell-jingling race around the globe.

Santa remembered feeling both relief and exhilaration in his eagerness to be off – so much happiness to be shared with all the good little girls and boys! His heart had thumped proudly as he saluted the loyal elves – then, in a twinkling, off they'd dashed into the sky, the reindeer heading south by south-east.

Later, turning in for a brief sleep before dawn broke, Santa and Mrs. Claus heaved a huge sigh of relief – all was well and tomorrow was a brand new day.

Story 2

Big Ideas
At The Pole

(Christmas Morning Surprises!)

Nelwyn

Zephyrs whisper up from the South, swirling glorious warmth and sunshine ahead of them into all the nooks and corners of the North Pole. Sweeping over sleek reindeer grazing in a lush meadow, they coast past Snowflake Village and the cottage of the Mahood triplets, tickling the three silver tails of their shooting-star weathervane and setting them a-jingle.

Behind this cottage, two teenaged elves are busy with hoe and shovel trying to gouge furrows in the hard earth. It is slow work for the ground is stony and the soil meager. Welwyn and Selwyn Mahood dig on, but by mid-afternoon they have scratched out only four long shallow ruts.

Holding a tape measure, squinting his eyes, Selwyn works out where the "sunny side" lies. Says he, "All the sunlight short summer will bring must fall on these furrows we've marked out with string".

What are these teens working at so steadily – long past dinner time and on into the dusk?

Why such earnest concentration on their youthful features?

Often last winter, snug by their fires,
The young elves had noticed the aches of their sires.
Knees and shoulders and fingers gave pain –
Coldness each year proved a terrible bane.

Woolly shawls, woolly socks, woolly mittens and slippers
(Things rarely seen on the younger nippers),
The old 'uns wore indoors to ward off the chill;
Winters were cruel to the feeble and ill.

With Christmas Day past, open weeks lay ahead
In which families threw parties and couples were wed.
Home improvements were always encouraged –
Helpful initiatives NEVER discouraged!

In North Pole Januarys, no time was lost,
Tools were repaired, broken blades tossed.
Wee elfins were shown by their Mammas and Grans
How to finish new goods with their own little hands.

Dyeing and knitting and quilting in bees,
They buzzed through their lessons, the ABCs;
"A" stood for always, "B" stood for be
And "C" was whatever it wanted to be……

"Consistent" and "careful", "contented", too,
"Clever" and "cheery" – "C" grew and grew.
All of the letters had lessons attached,
The Mothers and others never relaxed –

Teaching the little ones proper technique
So their work would be special and even unique.
Their motto, stitched large by fingers parental:
"One cannot succeed without fundamentals".

After alphabet lessons, to numbers they passed,
Knitting and sewing things meant to last.
Dividing and adding, subtracting too,
They purled and stitched until they knew

How to alter a pattern, its size and its shape
To dress a wee doll or line Superman's cape.
They mended and darned - took lunch to the old
Held captive by snowfall inside from the cold.

The young elves, likewise, were shown by their Dads
How to set up a workshop and tell bolts from brads.
They were taught to use saws and planes and lathes –
Learned the truth of the Motto that "Safety Pays".

Shown how to read blueprints and alter plans,
They could downsize toys for tinier hands.
The lads cleared sidewalks and carried in wood
Because footing was poor in the neighbourhood.

Online garden sites bursting with blurbs
Proclaimed the wonders of curative herbs –
Poultices, salves, and infusions galore
Could ease aching joints and so very much more!

In a trice, the youngest Mahood boys knew
That *this* summer, what they wanted to do
Was to grow an herb garden and offer their aid
To the elders whose aches were a constant parade.

While his brothers were planning their herbal plot,
Nelwyn was struck by a novel thought;
Hiking through stands of alder and beech
He'd noticed that Nature had lessons to teach:

Nothing was wasted, nothing unused,
Order and purpose and beauty were fused.
A desire had grown in him all winter long –
He determined to right a recurring wrong,

For too much timber was felled each year
To use in the Shoppes they all held dear,
While some was kept back to make repairs
To their cuckoo clocks or creaky stairs

The bulk of it went to make Christmas toys
From sailboats to swing sets for girls and boys.
They just couldn't risk running short of supply
But waste was vexing – made grown elves sigh.

In the new year when warehouse tallies were in
The thrifty elves saw to their chagrin
That a lot of fine wood would go to waste -
Lack of space meant it blazed in the fireplace.

Nelwyn mused while totting up how much wood

The workshops required and how they could

Harvest the trees and use every part,

For Recycling was the project dear to his heart.

But how could one do it? Use up every part?

Nelwyn was not sure where he should start

But he'd axe the trees needed for Christmas itself

AND help his elders, resourceful elf!

He smiled.

Time to THINK BIG!

GREAT PLANS lead to GREAT ACTIONS!

By early June, as supplies from all over the globe began to trickle in to the
North Pole warehouse, extra requisitions were noticed on the order sheets:

    1 dozen large wooden barrels

    12 hand scoops

    15 lbs. paraffin

    5 lbs. of gold glitter

    3 rolls of chicken wire in LARGE, medium and fine calibres

    1/2 dozen large tarpaulins

    yards and yards of bright Christmas ribbon

    3 mallets

    1 wood chipper and

    1 generator (small) to run it

The Master Supply Elf scratched his balding head. All these orders were signed
by Nelwyn Mahood. What was the lad up to?

Swamped as the sheer volume of arriving inventory snowballed, the MSE never did find time to have a word with Nelwyn. Thus, the supplies for the young elf were duly delivered to the small workshop/shed he had constructed behind their cabin (on the shady side of the yard away from "the garden").

Nelwyn set to work.

He built three wooden boxes side by side
Behind the shed, each four feet wide.
He topped them with screens of various gauges,
His plan was to compost in three distinct stages:

First, into Box I through the LARGE wire screen
Went all the raw scraps that had formerly been
Unused or wasted (so Nelwyn thought) –
Step 1 on the way t'ward the outcome he sought.

Pine needles, leaves and dried reindeer droppings,
Sawdust layered on kitchen choppings,
A dusting of earth, then water, then worms
Were left so Nature could start to turn

This unused waste into bountiful soil
(And bring success to this summer's toil).
He turned it once, adding leafy debris
To ensure that Box I was as full as could be.

Two weeks later, he sieved I into II –
Through the medium screen, almost all passed through!

He refilled Box I with the usual waste
And sought to establish a steady pace.

In two weeks more, Nel tipped II into III,
Lighter and finer, t'was plain to see
That the leavings had morphed into rich garden earth.
His big idea was proving its worth!

By July, the herb garden – tho' lovingly sown,
Had that stunted look that makes gardeners groan.
Selwyn and Welwyn had watered and weeded
But something was missing! Whatever was needed?

The rows of savory, hyssop and thyme
Were downright puny, far less than "prime".
Nelwyn led his two brothers aside
And showed them with some diffident pride

What he had done – his idea's birth –
Composting scraps to improve their earth.
They were going to use up Nature's trees
To kick-start the herbs for medicinal teas!

Welwyn and Selwyn hastened to spread
Nelwyn's beautiful soil on their garden's bed.
Now nourished and watered the plants shot up tall
All through late summer and into the fall.

Butterflies danced and bees hovered near,
Their droning and buzzing were pleasing to hear.

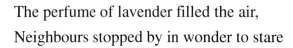

The perfume of lavender filled the air,
Neighbours stopped by in wonder to stare

At the fragrant growth springing out of this bed.
None could remember – or so they said –
Ever seeing so many magnificent plants.
The compliments made the Mahood boys dance!

Even Ratty Russ, the rural runt,
Whose complaining made everyone bear the brunt
Of his biting tongue, could do naught but praise,
"Niver seen the like in all me days!"

As the triplets spat grape seeds at dusk one night,
An errant shot led to a singular sight;
A whopping honeycomb, hidden from view,
Clung to their eaves – a wonder that few

Had ever seen on a North Pole street -
Its lavender honey would be a sweet treat!
By September, rosemary leaves and blooms
Had been gathered and hung up in their storeroom.

Garlic, oregano, mint and thyme
Were tied into bundles, drying in lines
Atop long trestles in the cool dark shed
Waiting for use in the weeks ahead:

Fresh herbs for the stewpot and mint for tea,
Lavender in packets to keep moth-free
The bedding and woollens of the senior elves.
O, Welwyn and Selwyn felt pleased with themselves!

They could now provide help for bronchitis and flu,
Earaches and bruises and chapped lips too,
But their biggest goal and the garden's key
Was to offer their elders Arthritis Tea.

When herbs were reaped and their plot at rest,
The younger lads went to their brother and asked
What they could do as the days grew cold
To help HIS dearest plan unfold.

Nel had used up first the needles and leaves
Now, on to the rest of Nature's fine trees:
"I'll need your help as my plan will reveal
In lots of muscle and oodles of zeal!"

All summer and fall into tarps on the ground
He'd thrown pine cones from trees that were recently downed.
Spread out in the sunlight, these cones opened wide
The elves shook the seeds out and set them aside.

With mallets the triplets crushed half the cones
Into sharp-edged pieces for outside the homes
Of ancient elves who spent nearly all
Their winters housebound for fear of a fall.

The chipper chewed up all the bark they could find.

Mixed then with cone bits, it formed a coarse grind.

The twelve wooden barrels were packed with these chips

Then shiny new scoops hooked on with brass clips.

To every street corner and all about town

The elves wheeled their barrels and hammered them down.

This grit was for spreading on streets and up stairs

BEFORE slipping on ice could cause fractures or tears.

The seniors gave ear to these newfangled plans

And gathered in groups – all the Grandpas and Grans

Thought it was wonderful – long overdue –

That streets could be safe with no salt residue.

Then in the spring with the icy ruts gone,

They'd rake up this mulch and spread it along

Garden beds in the village and out on the trails –

Even under the Library's colourful kales!

Radical Russ, that contrarian twerp,

Instantly sneered that their plan wouldn't work.

There'd be "too little grit and too much mess,

Too few spreaders and much distress"….

But when he paused at length and saw

How MUCH grit shot from the chipper's maw,

He knew it would last all winter through –

He shied off to buy sour lemons to chew.

Branches too small for the lumber mill
Were sturdy enough to be useful still,
Stripped of their bark and split into rails
They were lashed to form handholds on hiking trails.

Christmas loomed nearer. Hours drained away fast,
Tepid sun faded as weeks flew past.
Five weeks, a month, thirteen days upon
The calendar…determined, the elves pressed on.

Of the rest of the pine cones piled on the floor,
Some were for fires, the others "décor";
Half were dipped deep into hot melted wax
Then stuffed with sawdust and bundled in packs

To be stored by the elders – set on their hearths,
Saving trips to the woodpile when blizzards blew harsh.
Starting their fires would be easy and clean –
A practical side of Nelwyn's big dream!

The last cones were brushed and rolled gently through wax
Sprinkled with gold dust and set up on racks.
Pine and spruce boughs trimmed out in the cold
Awaited adornment, their chance to hold

The Christmas berries and glittering cones
Meant for Shoppe windows and front doors of homes.
Now, just four days remained before sleigh bells would ring
But without help they saw, Nelwyn's song wouldn't sing.

Pacing back and forth in the workshop, the triplets ruefully acknowledged their time and labour shortage. Santa's workshops always needed last minute help, so asking parents and peers was not an option. They thought and thought, then

I N S P I R A T I O N

off they set on the run.......

Watchful eyes set in a lean, narrow face noted an increase in the number of footprints leading to and from Mahood's garden shed. Even fresh snow could not hide the fact that the new tracks were coming from all over the village. With a mere two days before Christmas Eve, the snoop was determined to discover what exactly was going on behind that door.

Christmas Eve

A dark figure shoved open the wooden door and slammed it quickly shut behind himself. Open-mouthed in surprise, the occupants gaped as Ratty Russ' eyes darted about the shed and a look of utter confusion settled on his face.

"What's this now", he growled at the startled elves.
"What little secret have we kept to ourselves?
What's all the stuff hanging here in this shed?
It's Christmas Eve, why are you not home in bed?

Why have you done this? What's it all for?
And why were you all heading right for this door?

You'd better tell me and make it sharp
Or it will be hard to get home in the dark."

One tiny elva, all ready to leave
Shyly neared, eyeing a tear on his sleeve -
"Please, Mr. Ratty", said she soft and low,
"Let me mend your torn jacket and then we'll all go.

It's a secret you see, so we can't tell you all,
But if you'd come with us, it's a sure call
That we'll need some help before this night is through
And what we'll want is a TALL grownup like you.

We've used up every bough and berry
For things to make tomorrow merry.
All the Shoppe windows and cottage doors
Get a Christmas wreath – including yours."

Surrounded, astounded, dumbfounded (it's moot) -
Their dimples and grins rendered Russell mute.
Disarmed by their shyness and lack of guile,
Reluctant Russ crinkled a lopsided smile.

Cursed with a raspy, threatening voice,
Rejected Russ had had little choice –
His nature quiet and demeanor sad,
He'd made far fewer friends than other lads had.

These little ones – not knowing any of that –
Made him feel wanted right off the bat.
Before he could think of a way to say "No",
Reborn Russ became part of the show!

Whispering, hurrying – no laughter or shout
Betrayed them. Their secret must not get out –
They'd return in one hour, meet up at the shack,
Remarkably, Russ was the first one back.

Christmas morn….powdery snow drifts down from on high in shimmery veils.

Front doors begin opening – to a dazzling vision. On every door of every cottage up and down every street in Snowflake Village hangs a magnificent evergreen wreath.

Jewel-toned ribbons flutter alongside gleaming red berries and gold kissed pine cones. Boughs of spruce and pine braided with velvet ribbon garland every front porch.

In amazed silence, delighted smiles brighten the tired faces of the elves who have worked feverishly for so many weeks in Santa's workshops. Pulling shawls and jackets over their shoulders, one by one they trickle out into the street to promenade slowly up and down in wide-eyed pleasure. Murmuring, they find themselves converging in front of Santa's home where a beribboned lamp post crowned by a magnificent red-velvet-bow-topped wreath astounds them all.

As perplexed as the villagers, the Claus' join the crowd now winding its way downtown to the Community Hall where a roaring fire sends plumes of smoke straight up into the still air.

Welcoming warmth envelops them as they step inside where Welwyn and Selwyn Mahood have prepared a steaming cup to start off Christmas Day – hot chocolate with marshmallows for the young, simmering spiced apple cider for the parents, and Arthritis Tea for the elders.

Nelwyn Mahood, grinning broadly, rises and mounts the steps to the stage to speak. Santa and the villagers turn to hear him.....

"You have wakened this morn to a wondrous sight,
Some of our youngest worked into the night
To hang these wreaths for one and all,
Many thanks to those who answered our call.

As you probably know, my brothers and I
Started the year with hopes that were high.
I helped them and they helped me
But we needed more hands it was plain to see.

We found ourselves with mere days to go
With piles of boughs stacked out in the snow.
The day was saved by our younger elves
Who made garlands and wreaths all by themselves."

Nelwyn told the whole village how, four days before, he'd asked eleven giggling youngsters, aged five to eight, to meet him here at the Community Centre to ask for their help on his "Christmas Morning Project." In rapt silence the youngsters had listened as he unfolded his dream to them. At once they volunteered excitedly to help; sworn to secrecy, they set about making their plans.

Nelwyn drew laughter in noting that during the final hectic days leading up to Christmas, the parents of Snowflake Village somehow overlooked the fact that eleven of their offspring disappeared each day into a shed topped with a silver shooting star, emerging hours later smiling, hungry and mysteriously quiet. What unfolded was this:

Elvas, clever in snipping and sewing
Took scissors and ribbon when gales were blowing
To a long open table in Mahood's garden shed
To pleat and tie swags of velvety red.

Elves, skilled with wires and pliers and such
Set up a wee workshop with minimal fuss.
A clothesline and pulley stretched the length of the room
So work could be hung as it moved along.

Loops held forty-nine S – hooks up on that rope
In the few days left it was everyone's hope
That on Christmas Eve when the grownups were done
These youngsters would commence to have their fun.

Fine wire mesh was cut and bent into circular shapes secured with plastic ties so that no sharp edges could cut – (1 large and 48 medium). The yards of Christmas ribbon were tied into glorious bows of red, green, silver, gold and plaid. As one little elf snipped boughs of evergreen into proper lengths, two others – one in front and the other behind – tucked them securely into the wire frames with their small fingers. Each green wreath was then hung upon a hook on the clothesline.

Attaching clusters of red holly berries to wires, one of the 5–year olds fixed them to the boughs and pushed the wreath on to the next workstation. There, gold-dusted pine cones were wired in and the wreath was pushed on.

A wide wire loop was fitted to the top of each wreath so it could be hung safely from a front-door knocker, then a spectacular bow with trailing ribbons was centered and wired to the front to complete it.

One 8-year elva carefully measured and recorded the length of every handrail outside every Shoppe and cottage in town, then made swags of ribbon to suit. (She even measured the height of Santa's lamp post and recorded it).

Concluded Nelwyn,

"A special "thank you" from each of us
To a surprise volunteer – reliable Russ
Who set these wreaths upon every door
For which we'll be grateful for evermore."

Startled applause began to rise
Santa and others dabbed misty eyes.
Nelwyn announced each little elf's name,
Including friend Russ in this "Call of Fame."

Meanwhile, Nelwyn's brothers had a long trestle table covered with displays of their dried herbs and flowers. A huge kettle of fragrant Arthritis Tea was steeping next to them – delightedly, they refilled the empty cups of the grateful elders. Every family in Snowflake Village was presented with a small glass jar of lavender honey, hand labeled:

Nelwyn had yet a parting gift for every retired elf and elva leaving the Community Hall – from leftover pine branches he had carved and polished a fine walking stick. Each one had its rounded knob painted the same colour as its owner's front door, so that if accidentally forgotten outside the Candy Shoppe or the Library, it could be returned to the proper elf. The stick he presented to Santa was painted with three silver shooting stars all the way up its sturdy length.

Since Nelwyn and his brothers planned, come Spring, to sow and scatter the seeds collected from the pine cones, there was no part of any tree left unused.

The Mahood boys had made their dreams come true.

Thoughtfully stroking his beard, Santa slowly rose to his feet to address the throng, realizing that he had just witnessed a life lesson in behaviour from these young folk: he had always assumed that the elves' kind and gentle nature resulted from the emphasis that every adult placed on the virtue of harmony. This morning, he saw that the REAL lesson being learned by each youngster was to LOOK FOR THE OPPORTUNITY TO HELP ONE ANOTHER. When others succeeded, with help, harmony blossomed.

Knowing that help would be available when needed made every young elf un-afraid to ask for it.

Knowing that their advice and expertise were valued made every adult happy to share it freely.

Looking down from the stage of the Community Hall on all those dear, happy faces made Santa more grateful than ever to be living in their midst – and he told them so! He was deeply touched by their friendship.

Speeches finished, the villagers began to disperse to their homes to prepare for the traditional Christmas Morning Pancake Extravaganza – Mrs. Claus' specialty.

Radiant Russ would be escorted all day by a troop of ecstatic 5 to 8-year olds and later, in the finals of the Karaoke contest, Rocker Russ – blessed with a voice like a gravel road, WON, singing Rod Stewart's "Do Ya Think I'm Sexy"!

ARTHRITIS TEA

"A little of this and a little of that –
2 parts what you like
and
1 part less appealing"

Folklore

Ingredients:
Any of these

basil	peppermint
bee balm	rosemary
horehound	sage
hyssop	savory
lemon balm	spearmint
marjoram	thyme
oregano	

DIRECTIONS:
Pour boiling water over herbs and let stand 10-20 minutes before drinking.
(Most potent anti-arthritics are basil, marjoram, oregano and rosemary).

End of Story 2

Story 3

Welwyn and the Family Tree

(Back to the Beginning)

Welwyn

Part 1
The Very Beginning

Part 2
The Dark Years

Part 3
A Modern Christmas Tale

Part 1

Welwyn Mahood peers at the computer screen in the Snowflake Village library. He has been researching – or trying to research – his family tree, with NO success. There are zero references to "Elves" in the Geneological programs he has been scanning.

He had assumed that it would be an easy job, simply tapping in his surname in order to discover his ancestral history. The Christmas rush now over, this would have been a perfect time to ask Santa for the use of the mini-sleigh and a couple of reindeer to cross the Great Ocean and get the flavor of the "olde country". Welwyn has not mentioned his quest to his brothers, Nelwyn being heavily involved in recycling Christmas surplus and Selwyn busily concocting herbal brews for elves all over the village suffering with coughs and ailments.

Now, frustrated at the total absence of online material related to "Elves and their Antecedents", Welwyn heads home to ask his Mother and Dad what they know of the Mahood history.

Busy teaching five little elvas their ABCs, his Mother refers him to his Dad, who looks appraisingly into Welwyn's eyes when he hears the nature of the inquiry.

With quiet pleasure on his face and in his voice, his Dad says; "Welwyn, lad, I thought it might be you. I have been waiting, hoping that one of you boys would come to me about our family history. You see, son, it is ORAL. This means it never has been written down. Instead, one generation passes our story to the next and I have to tell you that committing this to memory requires a lot of time. Not everyone hearing it is willing to put in the effort. I am well pleased, that you have come now to ask about our roots. My Grandfather, the Mahood elder, still lives, as you know, and though his mind is somewhat clouded as to the present, his memory of the past

is crystal clear. There is yet an hour before lunch; would you like to go to his cottage with me and ask him to recount some of his early memories?"

Welwyn, the teenaged middle son of Oistin and Niamh Mahood, eagerly nods his head and follows his father out into the brittle cold of a North Pole January morning.

Their boots scrunch on the snow as around the corner to the home of Nedda Mahood they go. Welwyn's great aunt Nedda has cared for her father for many a year and she is pleased to see that Oistin and Welwyn have come on a mission. She correctly guesses that a request to hear the telling of the Family Tale is forthcoming.

Welwyn and his father bank up the wood they have carried in for Nedda's fire.

Happy to see them, she sets out tea and muffins on her polished wooden table, then leaves to go into the rear of the cottage. A short while later, Nedda reappears with an ancient, bent, bearded elf. Leaning heavily on two canes, he slowly makes his way to the chair set out for him. The old elf carefully settles his weight on to the padded cushion, then looks slowly over the tops of his spectacles, noticing for the first time, that there are others at his table.

The glow from the fire illuminates a wispy wreath of hair and a well-brushed beard framing a wrinkled round face. Two pink apple cheeks mound up whenever he smiles and intelligent light brown eyes regard them. Dignity rests like a cloak of ermine on his shoulders.

Great-aunt Nedda, speaking clearly, identifies his great-grandson Welwyn. Nodding slowly, Nevan Mahood smiles fondly at his grandson, then turns expectantly to Welwyn.

"Grandfather", begins Oistin, "I have brought you one who seeks to know more of our past. He is a good lad and I believe, worthy of your teaching."

The old eyes seem to pierce Welwyn's and look into his very soul. Accepting what was revealed there – kindness, honesty, determination, courage – Nevan

Mahood recognizes in the lad the characteristics of the ancient Mahood elders. His smile is gentle.

"I accept this young one, Oistin, he says, "and I am pleased that he has come to us, for I, too, have been waiting, hoping to teach the Tale one more time".

His eyes closed as he cast his mind back to the beginning. Speaking in cadence, he begins……

Through the mists of time long years ago
When the world was new and the sky was old,
A band of elves came forth by sea
Their object plain: WE WOULD BE FREE.

Through hardship and hunger they persevered;
Their goal escaped them for over a year.
Until they encountered a wooded isle
Where they trudged inland mile after mile.

To caves in a valley they made their way
Overlooking a river, beside a deep bay.
Their leader surveyed things with knowing eyes.
A decision was made by William the Wise:

He saw meadows of green with forests nearby –
Here they could live and here they could die
In peace, without fear of famine or drought,
Yes, here they would settle without any doubt.

William's search was for safety, a place in which all
The elves were sworn to heed this call:

"No Matter the Kinship – Whether Neighbour or Brother
Elves and Elvas Alike Are to Help one Another."

In hot days, they descended to camp by the stream.
Here William helped others to live out his dream
Of settling the land in this one small place
Living in harmony, working to face

Each day with hope in freedom hard won…
In time, leadership passed to Ennis, his son.

In the time of Ennis, elves gathered and fished
But their caves were cold and so they wished
For dwellings down off the rocky heights
With safety for all through the primal nights.

Thus Ennis devised a circular plan
For a village set on a rise of land –
Drew a plot on the ground for all to see
Then called all to work with vigour and speed.

Through the weeks and months they toiled with a passion
Felling trees – setting posts – in order to fashion
Something they'd never known firsthand –
Safe shelters for ALL in their brand new land.

Toward camp centre led all the streets
So any attacks by marauding beasts

Could be fended off at the outer rim
While women and elders hid babies within.

By the end of ten moons, they'd built a stockade
The dwellers inside it felt safe from a raid.
They had wood hewn for fires, meat drying on racks
Fish in the nets and hides on their backs…

Three generations flourished in this promising place, while, in due time,
changes were made:

Wooden gates could be opened and dragged shut at night.
Central fires crackled, throwing heat and light.
Now Langford the Laughing with knowing eye,
Encouraged folk to gather nigh –

With drums and flutes they danced and played,
Seldom – if ever – in all of their days
Could any remember having "fun" –
Together they revelled, "many" merged into "one".

Langford foresaw that there might come a day
When crowded living could lead the way
To strife between neighbours – unless a creed
Could be set down for all, AND ALL AGREED.

"Equal for equal" was what he proposed.
Every elf listened. None was opposed.

If one needed meat and another had hides,
They would barter 'til each one was satisfied.

Seasons passed. The village prospered in this meadow by the bay.

Up in the caves after elf folk had gone,
Weldon the wizard looked hard and long
Out on the plain where the great herds roamed
Then down in the village the elves now called home.

He could sense change coming, envision the day
When the herds would move on and the elf folk stay.
So with charcoal lumps he lined and drew
From memory, all the shapes he knew;

A bison, a deer, two parallel bands –
Once he traced his own two hands –
Weldon would teach them through art and song
That one elf is weak but many are strong.

He summoned them up to the cave that year
In the coldest season, so all might hear
From EACH OTHER what success each family had
Or offer solace when the going was bad.

When they'd settled in kin groups all 'round the fire
Long white-haired Weldon was deeply inspired.
Their old tales told of Flight and Pain –
Weldon vowed to prevent its happening again.

For each clan he'd whittled a thin stick of wood
Coloured and notched so each member could
See his own totem when the sticks were bound
Tightly together, lashed 'round and round;

Each family's elder solemnly accepted its new totem and in the light of the
flickering flames, before all, declared that he would protect and care for other clans
as if they were his own. Now Weldon gathered up all the single sticks and bound
them tightly together with animal sinew. All eyes on him, marshalling every ounce
of his strength, Weldon smashed that sheaf of sticks down across his knee.
The sheaf did not break.

Holding the bundle aloft, old Weldon pled;
"You MUST remember when I am dead:
It is vital that our history last
Or else we repeat the mistakes of our past.
One stick can be broken but MANY ARE STRONG
My art will stay here but our bond MUST go on.
From youngest to oldest you each have a task,
Should one elf wish help, he need only ask.
If threats arise from within or without,
You must ALL confer and work matters out".

Now by torchlight they shared their drink and food,
In a spirit of oneness – exactly the mood
Wise Weldon hoped each would carry away
And use in life, day after day.

Seasons have cycles, this they all knew.
Following snow, the sky would turn blue,
Showers coaxed green shoots forth from the ground
Soon berries and nuts would be easily found.

To secure enough meat, the younger elves roamed
While the elders remained and secured their homes.
All could see the village increasing in size
Amongst themselves, therefore, they deemed it wise

To set food aside for the dark cold days
And stockpile wood for their warming blaze.
Straightaway they set about doing just that –
Fish were dried on a smoking rack,

Fallen nuts were gathered and stored
In leather bags sewn to hold this hoard,
Yes, mouths would need feeding, they'd be prepared
And whatever they had would be evenly shared.

As the seasons circled 'round, saplings grew into stands of sturdy trees between
the meadow and the sparkling blue bay.

The rivers always rose with each spring's rain.
A middle-aged fisherelf perched by the stream
Watched intently as an uprooted tree
Rolled over the shallows – pushed, he could see

By the river's force. Sparkling sunlight shone
On to the droplets, one by one.
Dropping and plopping from the highest part
Of the root ball, as the trunk rolled over the heart
          ....of the sandbar....
Over....and over......and slowly......over.
Water dripping from the exposed roots.
Thus was born an idea that would change their lives
FOREVER.

Yuli the Younger was that watching elf.
He took off one boot and tried himself
To imitate what he had just seen;
The roots lift water up: what it would mean

If he, too, could bring water up on to the land.
He leaned to the river, filled the boot in his hand
He stood, raised his arm in a gradual arc –
Out spilled the water just past the high part.

He did it again and again. The water came up and it spilled. Sunbeams twinkled
on his little cascade. Round and slowly 'round his arm went –

                    Yuli hurried home.

To the forest he ran with axe and blade.
Four saplings were hewn and a round shape made.
Braided together with sinews strong,
He lashed two stout branches one cubit long

To the top of his circle, sticking out
And fixed in position his soaking boot.
To the river he bore it with curious throng,
Turned it into the current and rolled it along.

Circle turned. Boot filled. Water lifted. Water spilled.

In a few days more, he'd enlarged his wheel –
For lifting water it proved ideal.
None could believe it started with roots
But gladly his friends gave him all of their boots!

Yuli now found an enormous tree
Next to the river where he could see
That one thick branch overhung the flow –
He centered his wheel there. The first turn was slow…

Neighbours smiled as they flocked to see
What benefits could be had from a wheel on a tree!
All the boots fixed to the outer rim
Were lifting water – a tribute to him

Who was tired of searching the endless plain
For food – then walking all the way home again.
If they had their own water, they could make things GREEN.
Yuli nodded – happier than he'd ever been.

After a few more years passed, improvements to the wheel produced big changes in the meadow where they lived.

In the dark icy days, the elves planned what to sow
When the wheel would turn and the water flow –
Now lifted from the river in leather pails
It cascaded down ditches to nearby fields.

Grasses and gourds and nut trees flourished
Berries grew fat where their bushes were nourished.
The elves grew content and found that they could
Find time – and had talent – for carving wood.

Stools and ladders, sharp arrows and knives –
The elves worked hard to improve their lives –
Ropes were woven from sinews strong
So that loads could be lifted or dragged along.

Reeds were gathered for sleeping mats,
Hides cured for fashioning jerkins and hats,
Hollowed out logs became fishing boats,
Animal pelts sewn into warm winter coats.

Elvas strung beads made of bone and shell,
Decorated hides with dye and quill,
Lutes and drums and flutes were played
As life improved with the things they made!

Then, from their midst large of foot and body,
There emerged the infamous Naisbitt – the noddy –
Due to his sloth and unprincipled ways,
The village ended in smoking haze.

Naisbitt forgot that for leaders, "Work Comes Before Play."
Through holes in the nets silver fish slipped away.
Gaps in the stockade were stuffed with brush.
Maintaining the wheel, he said, was "no rush".

So weeds filled the ditches and choked out the grain
All through that summer fell too little rain.
Hunting for game forced elves further afield –
Rats in the storehouse fought and squealed

Over the shriveled nuts and roots left there.
As leaves turned to red a slavering bear
Trailed by starving half-grown cubs
Clawed through the stockade. Cudgels and clubs

She brushed off in her frenzied search for food.
Desperate elves did all they could –
With flaming torches they drove her back
But embers sparked wildly from thatch to thatch.

Fire roared through the streets where water skins
Hung limp and empty. Hot ashy winds
Drove the elves out into fiendish night
Where instinctively they clambered up the heights.
and huddled within the ancient cave.

Breathless, and stricken – leaderless, too,
They numbered now just fifty-two.
Their folly overwhelmed then. Some quietly cried
To think of the number of kin who had died.

Forlornly, they gathered some wood for fire

And confronted events – not just "bad" but "dire".

With minds now sharpened by guilt and fear

They drew close together, desperate to hear

a plan – some saving idea – what they should DO.

BUT

Some wanted to stay, some wanted to flee,

There was no course of action on which all could agree.

Some wanted to sail, some wanted to roam

Since there was no place left for them to call home.

From deep in the cave came excited cries

An older elf beckoned them – tears in his eyes –

"You MUST come at once and see this art

For these sacred caves were always part

Of our history, but WE LOST OUR WAY.

Now take heart, I stand before you this day

And I remember now what I heard as a lad

What we were to do when times got bad:

We must talk together 'til we find a plan.

We must work together so that we all stand

As ONE – for only then can we

Use all our skills in order to be

Able to face what the new dawn brings….

Come now, let us consider these things….."

They buried the dead of their elfin clan
Then, moving together, the unified band
Turned its back on the past, took a journey long
For "one elf is weak but many are strong."

At this point, great-aunt Nedda gently interrupted.

"Oistin, Father must have lunch and a rest before he continues. Could I ask you and Welwyn to return a little later this afternoon?"

END OF PART 1

PART 2

For years and long years, this band of survivors and their descendants wandered the island, seeking a haven where they again could set down roots. They regained confidence, honing the skills they needed to feed and defend themselves in the wild.

There was one young elf, taller than the rest who gradually assumed leadership of the band. Eventually, fourteen families approached Bryn – for this is how he was called, Bryn the Bold – wishing to turn and find their way back to the ruined settlement their families had once inhabited. They longed for the stream, the safety of the village – their old ways. Bryn called the band together. Patiently, they conferred, sharing their belongings and ideas so this small group would have the best chance for survival. With Bryn's blessing, they splintered off, heading back in the direction of the river by the bay. There was one solemn oath Bryn asked them to swear. They readily agreed.

Meanwhile, the larger party moved ahead, coming eventually to a highland of densely wooded forest. Smiles brightened faces! There was safety here under this leafy canopy! Bryn declared his intention to settle here, and half those remaining also wished to halt their wandering ways and stay with him. The band gathered to help and share with each other again, then those preferring the open spaces pushed forward, having agreed to the same vow Bryn swore with the families heading back to the ruins.

The last and smallest group, eventually discovered and crossed an ice bridge, coming to a place where grazing antlered animals roamed as far as the eye could see. These northern elves, well pleased, had found their home.

In the century after the days of Bryn, the three colonies of elves withstood disease and hardship, the River elves barely able to survive the first few seasons. They lived again in the caves because there were too few able-bodied elves who knew how to construct a village inside a stockade. Under their leader, Arthur, they did set a water wheel in motion and thereafter grew crops and began to thrive. The clay they discovered near the river hardened when set near fire and in time, the River elves grew a reputation for their fine pottery bowls and vessels. Trading with tall bearded folk who glided into their bay after crossing the Great Ocean in long wooden ships, the settlement prospered, the River elves flourished.

The Highland elves, making their homes in the unspoiled forest, found that their ability in carving and building in wood made them highly sought-after carpenters. Huge mountain logs, too heavy to drag on land, were floated downriver where their inventive leader, Nevan, devised wagons with oversized wheels that could transport people and goods easily. Tables, benches, plows, ox yokes and such were trundled down to a clearing by the stream where folk gathered every new moon to barter and exchange news. They became known as the Oak Wood elves.

The last remaining colony and the smallest in number, migrated farthest from the site of the disastrous fire and began to tame some of the deer that shared the great northern plain with them. Useful for riding and hauling and a source of hide, meat, bone and antler, these deer became the prized possession of the elves who herded them south to greener pastures in cold weather and led them north again in spring. Their leader, an elva named Jeneviere, had a calming way with the animals, knew how to tend them in calving; her people moved easily among them. The herd of tame deer enlarged each year, watched and protected by the elves. Trade in deer hides and their colourful weavings made these northern elves prosper. Bartering for sacks of small brass bells, the elves adorned their animals so that tinkling music floated out over the meadows every day. Life was good for these peaceful, clever elves; their numbers increased. They became known as the Tundra elves.

Within a few generations, the tall horn-helmeted folk who sailed the rivers and the Great Ocean had traded with all three elf colonies. They carried word to the Tundras of wagons, carvings and baskets made in the south. To the River elves, they told of great herds of tame animals whose meat and hides did not have to be hunted. They praised the ingenious large-wheeled wagons of the Oak Wood elves which could be backed into the shallows for off-loading cargo from ships, or fitted with runners to glide over snow filled trails in winter, and slide through muddy mountain passes in spring.

Curious about these other elves, the Tundras selected a young herdsman named Odell to travel south in search of those folk described by the traders. As a token of sincerity, they entrusted to Odell one of their precious totem sticks. Wrapped in soft rabbit fur, it nestled in a leather pouch he tied around his thigh with lengths of sinew.

Odell's mission was to speak with the elders of both these colonies to determine if all three elfin colonies were descendants of the same distant ancestor.

The quest began before spring, while the ice bridge was still intact, and continued overland for fourteen long weeks. Using a crude map sketched for him by the Viking traders, Odell moved south by southwest towards the forests, living off the land as he went. Eventually, hiking through more trees than he ever knew existed, he was drawn by the sound of rushing water to a stream deep in the forest. Following its course, he stumbled upon wide cart tracks cutting a crude trail through the underbrush and followed those tracks into a neat, busy settlement in a sunny clearing.

Approached by smiling, curious villagers, Odell was taken to a nearby cottage to eat and rest, then escorted to the cabin of the calm elder who heard his story.

After listening thoughtfully, and examining Odell's crude map, the elder rose from his fireside chair to open a large, carved wooden chest. Carefully, from deep within a back corner, he lifted a slender package wrapped in soft fur. Dry mouthed,

Odell set his bundle on top of this chest and began to untie it. Opposite, the elder did the same.

At once they realized that the totems matched – faded paint and similar notching were unmistakable! One astonished face looked into the other, then gleeful shouts and excited back-slapping ensued! Jigging with joy, the elder dashed down his cabin steps to haul on the rope of the village bell with one hand – the other clutching Odell's sleeve as if to prevent him from vanishing. Elves and elvas streamed from their cabins and out of the forest on the run, surrounding their leader and the gonging bell. His face split with the widest of smiles, the elder clarioned the good news and asked that his eldest grandson be brought to him at once.

Astounded to be discovered by a long lost relative, the overjoyed villagers embraced Odell and they all feasted together into the night.

Greatly excited, Odell, with Emlyn, the seventeen year old grandson of Oak Wood's ecstatic elder, made ready the next day to resume his search for the River elves. Their legs hurried them down through the pristine wilderness that Emlyn knew well, then out on to the plain.

At length, after several more weeks, they could see by their map and the changing countryside that they were approaching the area where streams and a river emptied into a great bay. From afar they could just make out peaked rooftops and wisps of smoke rising from a chimney here and there. The shy herder and the quiet woodsman at his side looked down upon a seaport bustling in the midsummer sun. Could this be the spot settled by their ancestors so many long years ago?

A mill by the river's edge ground grain for flour. Bright banners fluttered from market stalls overflowing with fresh cheeses, fish, apples, onions, blankets, pottery bowls and steins – and the aroma of fresh baking bread made their dry mouths water. Carefully shouldering through the crowd so as not to appear rude, they made their wide-eyed way past a sheep auction to a booth where they asked for the elder. A passing elva led them directly to meet a portly, clear-eyed older elf – Stefan Stoutheart.

Having politely waited while the young messengers were given food and drink, Stefan was scarcely able to control his mounting excitement as they recited their journey and showed him their totems. He couldn't remember the last time he'd looked at the contents of the bundle his father had entrusted to him; now he rose and lifted it down from the mantel wrapped in its tattered hides.

A muffled gasp escaped his lips when he laid eyes on the contents. Tears formed in his eyes and flowed down his cheeks in mighty rivers as he turned to hold out his totem to them – a match in every way.

He clutched the young elves to his chest, overcome. Clearly, this was a miracle! Their spirits soared, united in joy: Yes – a miracle!

Now there lived at the river an elf of renown,
Michael the Modest was how he was known.
He was Mayor of the townsfolk and managed the port
Established the laws and set up a court.

He carefully saw to commercial affairs –
Made sure that trade flourished, was fully aware
That if fines were levied, fines were paid.
What worked for one worked for all, he said.

Michael's father Stefan (also called Stout)
Had fervently hoped 'fore his days were out
To meet again with their long lost kin
Whose stories they'd heard, though memory was dim.

So Michael sent messengers forth in the fall
Inviting elf elders to come and bring all

Their families to Rivertown one year hence –
A reunion of elfdom was about to commence.

• •

For the tundra elves driving their huge herds south
The call was welcomed and spread by mouth –
To all the reaches of their vast domain
Reunion was coming! Together again!

Deep in the forest, word was received –
After so many ages, could scarce be believed!
All through the mountains happiness reigned –
Reunion was coming! Together again!

Rivertown declared games and a welcoming feast,
Improvements began – work scarcely ceased!
They renamed Main St. "Memory Lane"
Reunion was coming! Together again!

• •

The months slipped by……..

With irony bitter, good Michael died
Just past his prime, swept out on the tide.
His plans were made and already in motion
When his ship went down in the uncaring ocean.

An older elva stepped forth 'midst this sorrow
Counselling that "to cope with tomorrow
We must handle each day one by one
What else can we do? The clans will come

And we must be ready to do our best.
Michael would want this, in peace may he rest.
Let us now resume, for duties we have,
And after the "Welcome", we climb to the cave".

The overriding hope in this gathering of peers
Was to piece together the missing years,
Learn from each other their triumphs and trials
And rekindle relations despite the miles.

Annibal, the elva who had urged them on,
Possessed an asset with which she'd been born –
Memories of tales told to her when small
She could recite by heart with perfect recall.

The rumble of wagons was heard at last,
Rising dust showed that travelers had passed
The dry plain and were headed to Rivertown.
Feverish joy could not be tamped down.

Cheers, tears – running to see
If their long lost kin were here indeed –
Embracing delightedly, many wept
Seeing come true a dream they had kept

Alive in their hearts through centuries long
Knowing, in the vast world they did belong
Together as family, from the same Family Tree
Smiles and tears mixed in the happy melee.

Only one day later, bells jingling, horns blaring,
The Tundra elves found themselves smothered in caring
Loving arms – surrounded on every side
By cheering kin from far and wide.

This jubilant, dancing, triumphant mass
Entered Rivertown – one at last,
To be welcomed by Stefan, eyes filled with tears
At being truly united after three hundred years.

Following two full days of feasting and greeting,
All elves desired their communal meeting.
All those souls whose ancestors fled
The Great Fire, and whose destinies spread

Over forests and tundras to the west and north
Eons ago when they'd had to set forth,
Lived through diseases and extremes of weather
Had dreamed of this – once again coming together.

Quietly, solemnly they climbed the heights to the cave.

Settled in their three groups, distinguished by costume but surprisingly similar in appearance, the elves turned to look toward the fire being kindled in the center of the cave. By the light of licking flames, a few of the cave paintings were illuminated. Elves and elvas alike were struck dumb to see this precious art known to them only through the old tales.

The elders of the Tundra, Oak Wood and River elves rose to their feet. A hush fell over all present like a shawl snugged up reassuringly around shoulders. Gravely, each elder produced the ancient sticks of his own clan. A gasp of comprehension rose as the elf folk saw their ancestral totems together again.

Harry the Honest, the oldest elf present, grasped the totems, and with hands that shook slightly, bound them tightly into a bundle. Six hundred and three pairs of eyes focused on the totems held aloft in Harry's hand. Six hundred and three hearts trembled at understanding that they were in the presence of the spirits of the old ones. Truly, the stories passed down to them were REAL.

A tear slowly traced its way down Honest Harry's lined cheek; his voice trembled but then lifted and he began to recount what he had been taught. Surely, confidently, his voice rose as his words, then Annibal's perfectly blended…….

END OF PART 2

PART 3

After Reunion, Olin rose to fame
At Rivertown, which enlarged and became
The busiest port in all the northeast.
Writers and painters never ceased

Creating brochures and advertising
For businesses good at analyzing
What goods were needed, where, and when
Trading expanded for all of the kin.

Barter with Oak Wood flourished and grew –
Grandfather clocks and dining suites, too,
Were ordered and shipped 'way over the seas,
Businesses grew. Elders were pleased.

Likewise leather and hides from the north
Were ordered by city folk sallying forth
In wintertime, sporting reindeer coats
Matched with hand-stitched Tundra Totes.

Newspapers and catalogues far and near
Sang the praises of elvin gear,
But buying and selling was not in their charter
The elves preferred to talk and barter.

'Bout this time in their history, not needing money
The elves came to hear of a soul so sunny
That they convened, then sent a delegation
To see him, thinking "amalgamation".

For what they'd heard was amazing – if true.
Prime Elf Odhrin, to give him his due,
Sleuthed about to learn what info he could
In order to see if this Nicholas would

Be quite suitable for working with them,
In assisting folk (making it CLEAR to him),
That wee folk won't work with just ANYONE –
They have no guile, so their trust must be won.

Odhrin sent Derrie, his trusted brother,
To assess the character of this generous "other"
Who reputedly helped both young and old
If they were GOOD – the very mold

Elves admire in people everywhere;
Good humour, sharing, and patient care
Of those who on earth are not richly blessed
But despite this, do their Very best.

What Derrie told Odhrin made his heart delight.
This Nicholas, though, was quite a sight!
When they met, by appointment, in the month of May,
The smallish elf was swept away

By the appearance before him LARGE and ROUND
Of this friendly giant whose face was crowned
With the broadest smile he had ever seen.
Derrie relaxed – if he had ever been

Unsure of the motives or the reasons why
Nicholas helped others – one look in his eye
Revealed oceans of kindness – he instantly knew
That a merging of equals could shortly ensue.

Nicholas, smiling, replied that he
As a lad, had learned that he could be
A much better person if he crossed out "I"
And put "others" first – meeting folk eye to eye.

He was curious to know why Derrie had come.
"You elves are many and I am but one;
Why do you seek me who helps when he can,
When you can do good for so many men?"

The answer surprised but Nick saw it was true
Derrie said their clans had all been through
So much separation for much of their past
That they yearned to unite and make it last.

Nicholas and Derrie sat down to discuss the particulars then left for their homes; Nicholas to ponder with his plump wife the implications of partnership with the elves, and Derrie to report to Odhrin and a council of the clan elders. A letter of invitation to Rivertown was couriered to the Oak Wood and Tundra Elves:

Our clans are successful but still far flung

Reunion once yearly is a hardship for some.

We elves are approaching a fork in the road

And Nicholas is willing to share our load.

Come meet him – save this special date –

As we vote on a motion to affiliate.

August 6
RSVP

The agenda was set. Grand Council was called
Elves and elvas alike were completely enthralled
At a notion of moving to the far far north
Where Nicholas, yearly, could go forth

In a sleigh drawn by reindeer from the Tundra herds
Bearing gifts for Good Folk whose thankful words
Were the only reward they desired to hear
In mid-winter. Such a spiritual time of year.

Winter solstice, to the ancients up in the cave,
Was the time they'd elected to gather, and aid
Each other – sharing bad times and good –
Celebrating their bond with drink and food.

Aye, this sacred time of the elfin year
Coincides neatly with Christmas cheer.
Good wishes and carols ring out anew
And families unite as they're meant to do.

Though generations have come and gone,
The partnership north of us carries on.
Goodness and Joy are St. Nick's cause
(You probably know him as Santa Claus)

But the name we call him matters not
For kindness and love are primarily thought
To be, by far, the most cherished part
Of this time of year special in everyone's heart.

Smiling as he always did after reciting the Santa Tale and their Family Tree, old Nevan opened his eyes in satisfaction to gaze around his table. Nedda and Oistin beamed at him but there was total incomprehension written all over the wide-eyed face of Welwyn….

"There lad", said his father, "most of us feel that way when we first hear the telling of the Tree. It's a lot to take in all at once, which is why it is usually spread out over several "sittings"."

Finally, regaining his speech, Welwyn stammered,

"But Dad, how is this our Family Tree? The Mahood Family Tree?"

Oistin patiently set about his explanation while Nedda rose to put on the kettle for more tea. Nevan's old eyes smiled, for he too, loved hearing this part:

"Fifteen years ago, as Christmas approached and our favourite time of the season was upon us, it became clear that your Mother would give birth at any moment. As it happened, you and your brothers arrived on Christmas Eve. How excited we were! And how blessed we felt to welcome healthy triplets!! We gave you very special names in honour of the occasion; you see Welwyn, your name IS the Family Tree.

All elves and elvas are given the same middle name as a reminder of the hardships and desperate times our families endured during the dark years apart. None of us EVER wishes to go through that experience again.

Our middle name, BANJOES, thus reminds us of

B – Bryn the Bold, who led the survivors after the Great Fire

A – Arthur, who resettled elves at the River site and restarted the water wheel

N – Nevan, who invented the wagons of the Oak Wood elves, the early versions of Santa's sleigh

J – Jeneviere, who tamed the reindeer of the Tundra and whose offspring pull Santa's sleigh to this day

O – Odell, the first messenger sent forth to find the lost kin

E – Emlyn, the messenger who joined Odell and who helped locate the River settlement

S – Stefan, who with his son Michael, reunited all three clans

A glimmer of comprehension crept into Welwyn's eyes and a smile began to turn up the corners of his mouth.

"Oh, Dad, I get it! I get it! The letters of our names STAND for those who have gone before!"

Nevan chuckled as his tea was poured.

Nedda and Oistin pointed at Welwyn and chimed in unison;

"W – is for William the Wise

E – is for Ennis, his son

L – is for Langford the Laughing

W – is for Weldon the Wizard

Y – is for Yuli the Younger

N – is for Naisbitt, the fool.

M – is for Michael the Modest

A – is for Annibal the elder

H – is for Honest Harry

O – is for Olin, the re-uniter

O – is for Odhrin, the Prime Elf and

D – is for Derrie, his brother, who together realized that our future and Santa's lay together for "Good"!"

Pride, astonishment, and joy were evident all over the speechless lad's face – he could barely contain himself! As he cast his memory back over what he had heard, he found that he had two questions.

"Dad, what does Nelwyn's "N" stand for, and Selwyn's "S"?"

Oistin gazed lovingly at his grandfather and spoke gently,

"You know that my parents died in a forest fire when I was a toddler, and that I was raised by Grandfather. Your elder brother, therefore, is named for Nevan, this finest of elves. He makes me proud to be a Mahood. Your younger brother is named for Santa who remained by our sides all through your Mother's labour until each babe was safely delivered. He makes me proud to be called his friend.

There was a short silence.

Nevan cleared his throat and asked quietly,

"There is another question, Welwyn?"

"Yes, Great-grandfather; when Bryn led the survivors of the Fire on the great plain, they split into three groups – some went back to the River, some settled in the forest and some roamed the tundra. What was the oath he asked them all to swear?"

"You have listened carefully. I am pleased, Welwyn – you will make a fine student of the Tree. Bryn's oath was this, that every year in the darkest, coldest days of winter, we would gather in peace to share a meal together. We vowed to honour the Ancient Ones who went before us, support each other through good times and bad, and teach our young ones that love is the greatest gift we have to share."

"Well", piped up Welwyn, "being part of this family is a pretty great gift, too!"

Laughing comfortably together, they sat at the wooden table, all the generations bound by their history and family ties.

THE END

Bibliography:

Buchman, Dian Dincin. "Herbal Medicine", Wings Books, div. of Random House, New York, Avenal, N. Jersey 1979, 1996

Castleman, Michael. "Nature's Cures", Rodale Press, Emmaus, Penn. 1996

Duke, James A. "The Green Pharmacy". Rodale Press, Emmaus, Penn. 1997

Ody, Penelope. "Home Herbal". Darling, Kindersley, London, New York, Stuttgart 1995

Stewart, Rod. "The Very Best of Rod Stewart", Warner Bros. Records, "Do Ya Think I'm Sexy", Warner Music Group, an AOL Time Warner Co. 2001 New York, N. Y.